THE

FLORAL

FORTUNE-TELLER;

A GAME

FOR THE SEASON OF FLOWERS.

BY

Miss S.C. Edgarton.

BOSTON:
PUBLISHED BY A. TOMPKINS.
1847.

*Published for the Supernatural Fox Sisters' Supernatural History
Series—collections of books and artifact reproductions focusing on
places and events in supernatural history.*

Cover adapted from Ephraim W. Bouvé lithograph from
original 1846 edition. Biodiversity Heritage Library.
Typesetting, editing, & design by Katie Fox.

Classic Reprint Paperback Edition

ISBN: 978-1-947587-13-7

Design CC BY-NC 4.0 2020 by
Katie Fox
Fox Editing & Publishing
San Francisco, Ca.

FOXEDITING.COM

Stereotyped by
GEORGE A. CURTIS;
New England Type and Stereotype Foundry.

PREFACE.

THE custom of fortune-telling is nearly as old as time. Almost everything has been turned into an oracle. Even the dregs of a teacup have been supposed to possess the "gift of prophecy." Why, then, should not flowers, that are forever rising up, clothed with the mantles of prophets, and speaking in a language that has become as familiar as household words—why should not these little "floral apostles" be consulted respecting the mysteries of our earthly destiny?

At all events, they are pure and beautiful playthings for the fancy; and if any diversion on earth be innocent, it must be one whose instruments are poetry and flowers.

In selecting our oracles, we have drawn from the purest wells of English poetry; for who like Shakespeare can describe character,

or like Wordsworth, Coleridge and Tennyson, picture a scene? We have also turned over the pages of the great German dramatists, and here and there culled from them a word of wisdom, or of prophecy. Our aim has been to condense into our brief oracles as much point, wit and variety, as the interest of the game will permit.

How well we have succeeded in our attempt to please, will he best determined by the future success of this little book. God speed it on a harmless way!

KEY TO THE FORTUNE-TELLER.

THE following five questions are answered, respecting the character and future fortunes of an individual.

1. What is my character?

2. What is, or will he, the state or quality of my love?

3. What is, or will be, my worldly fortune?

4. What is the scene in which most of my life will be spent?

5. What is the character of my future companion?

The person consulting our little Fortune-Teller, must select a bouquet of five different colored flowers, of whatever kind he chooses. The White shall describe to him his character; the Blue, the state or quality of his love; the Purple, his worldly fortune; the Yellow, the scene in which his life shall be chiefly passed; and the Red, the character of his future wife.

For example; if a gentleman bring a white Lily, a blue Violet, a Foxglove, a Marigold and a red Rose, he will first turn to the catalogue of White flowers, where, under the head of Lily, he will find this description of his character:

"*Of a free and open nature,*

That thinks men honest that but seem to be so,

And will as tenderly be led by the nose

As asses are."

SHAKESPEARE.

The Violet, found in the catalogue of Blue flowers, will unfold the state of his "love matters" as follows:

*"You are now sailed into the north of my lady's opinion;
where you will hang like an icicle on a Dutchman's beard,—
unless you do redeem it by some laudable attempt."*

SHAKESPEARE.

The Foxglove will thus declare his worldly condition:

"Poor, but content, is rich, and rich enough."

SHAKESPEARE.

To learn the scene of his future abode he will consult the Marigold.

*"A cottage on a plot of ground,
With large prospect north and south."*

WORDSWORTH.

The Rose will reveal to him the character of his wife:

*"A woman in her freshest age,
Of wondrous beauty and of bounty rare;
Full of great love."*

SPENSER.

By different combinations of flowers, a great variety of fates may be unfolded. Nor is the purpose of the game wholly confined to the reading of fortunes. Any gentleman wishing to compliment a lady, may do it in a very delicate and poetical manner, by selecting a bouquet of flowers that shall express the good fortune he wishes her.

The first paragraph upon each page is for the Lady, the second for the Gentleman.

PART I.

WHITE FLOWERS.

Describing your Character.

APPLE-BLOSSOM.

A most fresh and delicate creature.
A most exquisite lady.

SHAKESPEARE.

Thou hast been
As one, in suffering all, that suffers nothing;
A man that fortune's buffets and rewards
Hast ta'en with equal thanks; and bless'd are those
Whose blood and judgment are so well commingled,
That they are not a pipe for fortune's finger
To sound what stop she pleases.

SHAKESPEARE.

APRICOT-BLOSSOM.

The world hath not a sweeter creature.

*　　　*　　　*　　　*

What an eye!—Methinks it sounds a parley of provocation.—
An inviting eye, and yet, methinks, right modest.

SHAKESPEARE.

An eye, like Mars, to threaten and command,
A combination and a form, indeed,
Where every god did seem to set his seal
To give the world assurance of a man.

SHAKESPEARE.

ANEMONE, OR WIND FLOWER.

Your eye is like the star of eve,
And sweet your voice as seraph's song.
*   *   *   *
Within your soul a voice there lives!
It bids you hear the tale of woe.

COLERIDGE.

Thou art not for the fashion of these times,
Where none will sweat but for promotion,
And having that, do choke their service up,
Even with the having; it is not so with thee.

SHAKESPEARE.

BACHELOR'S BUTTON.

———

Sell when you can; you are not for all markets.

SHAKESPEARE.

———✳———

Jealous in honor, sudden and quick in quarrel,
Seeking the bubble reputation.

SHAKESPEARE.

BALSAMINE.

———

Thou hast always been gentle and good.

BEAUMONT.

———✳———

A butterfly, a lord
Of flowers, garlands, love-knots, silly posies,
Groves, meadows, melodies and arbor-roses.

KEATS.

BLOOD ROOT.

———

You have deserved high commendation, true applause, and love.

SHAKESPEARE.

You have a nimble wit.
Your spirits are too bold for your years.

SHAKESPEARE.

CALLA.

———

Oh thou art fairer than the evening air,
Clad in the beauty of a thousand stars.

MARLOWE.

An ornament of nature, fine and polished,
A handsome youth, indeed!

FORD.

CANDY TUFT.

———

Handsome, young, and hast all those requisites that folly and green minds look after.

SHAKESPEARE.

><><*><><

You are one of those that will not serve God, if the devil bid you.

SHAKESPEARE.

CHINA ASTER.

———

Thou art as wise as thou art beautiful.

SHAKESPEARE.

><><*><><

Thy mind is a very opal! I would have men of such constancy put to sea, that their business might be everything, and their intent everywhere.

SHAKESPEARE.

CAMELLIA.

Of a constant, loving, noble nature.

SHAKESPEARE.

True of mind, and made of no such baseness
As jealous creatures are.

SHAKESPEARE.

CLEMATIS.

Of excellent discourse,
Pretty and witty; wild, and yet too, gentle.

SHAKESPEARE.

Believe me, in thy breast are thy destiny's stars. Trust in
thyself. Decision is thy Venus. The Malignant, the only one
that injures thee, is irresolution.

SCHILLER.

CANTERBURY BELL.

Faithful, gentle, good,
Wearing the rose of womanhood.

TENNYSON.

The gravity and stillness of your youth
The world hath noted, and your name is great
In mouths of wisest censure.

SHAKESPEARE.

COLUMBINE.

Ready in gibes, quick-answered, saucy, and
As quarrelsome as the weasel.

SHAKESPEARE.

You are rather point-device in your accoutrements; as loving
yourself than seeming the lover of any other.

SHAKESPEARE.

CHRYSANTHEMUM.

Thou art pleasant, gamesome, passing courteous,
But slow in speech, yet sweet as spring-time flowers.

SHAKESPEARE.

Thou art e'en as just a man,
As e'er my conversation coped withal.

SHAKESPEARE.

DAHLIA.

Thou canst not frown, thou canst not look askance,
Nor bite the lip, as angry wenches will;
Nor hast thou pleasure to be cross in talk;
But thou with mildness entertain'st thy wooers,
With gentle conference soft and affable.

SHAKESPEARE.

Stiff in opinions, always in the wrong,
Everything by starts, and nothing long.

DRYDEN.

DAISY.

A good lady, and a wise and virtuous.

SHAKESPEARE.

As gentle as zephyrs, blowing below the violet,
Not wagging his sweet head; and yet as rough,
The blood enchased, as the rudest wind,
That by the top doth take the mountain-pine,
And make him stoop to the vale.

SHAKESPEARE.

DAFFODIL.

A face with gladness overspread!
Soft smiles by human kindness bred!
And seemliness complete, that sways
Thy courtesies, about thee plays.

WORDSWORTH.

Full of ambition; an envious emulator
Of every man's good parts.

SHAKESPEARE.

ELDER.

***

God hath given you one face, and you make yourself another;
you jig, you amble, you lisp.

SHAKESPEARE.

***

The glass of fashion and the mould of form,
The observed of all observers.

SHAKESPEARE.

EVERLASTING.

***

A gentle maid, whose heart is lowly bred,
Whose pleasures are in wild fields gathered.

WORDSWORTH.

***

One of those gentle ones that will use the devil himself with
courtesy.

SHAKESPEARE.

HOLLYHOCK.

A shop of all the qualities that man loves woman for.

SHAKESPEARE.

A fellow of infinite jest, of most excellent fancy.

SHAKESPEARE.

HOUSTONIA.

A woman of a stirring life
Whose heart is in her house.

WORDSWORTH.

An unanimous mind, content
In the low vale of life.

COWPER.

HONEYSUCKLE.

The mercer's plague, from shop to shop
Wandering, and littering with unfolded silks
The polished counter, and approving none,
Or promising with smiles to call again.

COWPER.

Well read in poetry and other books,
Cunning in music and the mathematics.

SHAKESPEARE.

HAWTHORN.

Young, modest, meek and beautiful.

WORDSWORTH.

❧✻❧

In genius and substantial learning high;
For every virtue, every worth renowned.

THOMSON.

JASMINE.

I see the graceful, straight and tall,
I see the sweet and bonnie.

BURNS.

❧✻❧

As smooth
And tender as a girl, all essenced o'er
With odors, and as profligate as sweet.

COWPER.

LILY.

A miniature of loveliness; all grace
Summed up, and closed in little.

TENNYSON.

Of a free and open nature,
That thinks men honest that but seem to be so,
And will as tenderly be led by the nose
As asses are.

SHAKESPEARE.

LOCUST.

Beauty has corrupted thy heart. That
little face! shame on thee! In the morning
its splendor dies, its rose sheds its leaves.
Swallows that love in the spring-time fly
when the north-wind blows. Thine autumn
will frighten away thy lovers.

SCHILLER.

A very, very—peacock!

SHAKESPEARE.

LARKSPUR.

Your heart's like a child,
And your life like the new-driven snaw.

BURNS.

Wm.*~.

A pure ingenuous elegance of soul,
A delicate refinement known to few.

THOMSON.

LEMON.

Fresher than the morning rose
When the dew wets its leaves; unstained
As is the lily, and pure as the mountain snow.

THOMSON.

Thou art no Sabbath-drawler of old saws,
Distilled from some worm-cankered homily.
     *   Thou from a throne
Mounted in heaven wilt shoot into the dark
Arrows of lightnings.

TENNYSON.

LUPINE.

———

Sincere, plain-hearted, hospitable, kind.

THOMSON.

✥

A gentleman that loves to hear himself talk, and will speak more in a minute than he can stand to in a month.

SHAKESPEARE.

MALLOWS.

———

To be merry best becomes you; for out of question, you were born in a merry hour.

SHAKESPEARE.

✥

Content, and careless of to-morrow's fare.

THOMSON.

MYRTLE.

Thou wilt never get thee a husband if thou he
so shrewd of thy tongue.

SHAKESPEARE.

Rash, and very sudden in choler.

SHAKESPEARE.

ORANGE FLOWER.

A lady of most confirmed honor, of an unmatchable spirit, and
determinable in all virtuous resolutions; not hasty to anticipate
an affront, nor slow to feel, where just provocation is given.

LAMB.

A little, upright, pert, tart, tripping wight.

BURNS.

OX-EYE.

A wonder of this earth,
Where there is little of transcendent worth,—
Like one of Shakespeare's women.

SHELLEY.

A dreamer among men, indeed
An idle dreamer!

WORDSWORTH.

PEA-BLOSSOM.

A serious, subtle, wild, yet gentle being;
Graceful without design, and unforeseeing.

SHELLEY.

Thy looks, thy gestures all present
The picture of a life well spent.

WORDSWORTH.

PETUNIA.

Void of guile,
A lovely soul, formed to be blest and bless.

SHELLEY.

Sensibility to love,
Ambition to attempt, and skill to win.

WORDSWORTH.

PEONY.

A merry, nimble, stirring spirit.

SHAKESPEARE.

A man of letters and of manners too;
Of manners sweet as virtue always wears
When gay good nature dresses her in smiles.

COWPER.

PINK.

———

Rich in love and sweet humanity.

WORDSWORTH.

❧ ✻ ☙

Surpassed by few
In power of mind and eloquent discourse.

WORDSWORTH.

POPPY.

———

Nature never framed a woman's heart
Of prouder stuff.

SHAKESPEARE.

❧ ✻ ☙

A man in all the world's new fashion planted;
That hath a mint of phrases in his brains;
One whom the music of his own vain tongue
Doth ravish like enchanting harmony.

SHAKESPEARE.

POTATO.

———

Thou art divine, fair lady:
The hearts of men adore thee.

BURNS.

Of all men the best deserving a fair lady.

LAMB.

ROSE.

———

As fresh as the morning, the fairest in May;
As sweet as the evening among the new hay;
As blithe and as artless as the lambs on the lea.

BURNS.

A merrier man, within the limit of becoming mirth, 1 never
spent an hour's talk withal.

SHAKESPEARE.

SNOW-DROP.

To see thee is to love thee,
And love but thee forever;
For Nature made thee what thou art,
And he ne'er made sic' anither!

BURNS

Young in limbs, in judgment old.

LAMB.

STRAWBERRY-BLOSSOM.

Charming, sweet and young,
No artful wiles to win.

BURNS.

A kinder gentleman treads not the earth.

LAMB.

SNOWBALL.

———

A maid of grace and complete majesty.

SHAKESPEARE.

A unit; a thing without a name in the state; a something to be governed, not to govern.

LAMB.

SWEET-WILLIAM.

———

Never saw I mien or face
In which more plainly I could trace
Benignity and homebred sense,
Ripening in perfect innocence.

WORDSWORTH.

A fishing, hawking, hunting country gentleman.

LAMB.

SPIREA.

Thou art of so free, so kind, so apt, so blessed a disposition, that thou holdest it a vice in thy goodness not to do more than thou art requested.

SHAKESPEARE.

An affable and courteous gentleman.

SHAKESPEARE.

STAR OF BETHLEHEM.

A maiden never bold—
Of spirit so still and quiet, that thy motion
Blushes at thyself.

SHAKESPEARE.

Subtle, discerning, eloquent; the slave
Of Love, of Hate, forever in extremes;
Gentle when unprovoked, easily won,
But quick in quarrel—thro' a thousand shades
Thy spirit flits, chameleon-like; and mocks
The eye of the observer.

ROGERS.

SYRINGA

Most rich in gifts of mind,
Nor sparingly endowed with worldly wealth.

WORDSWORTH.

Of great estate, of fresh and stainless youth,
In voices well divulged, free, learned and valiant,
And in dimensions and the shape of nature
A gracious person.

SHAKESPEARE.

VERBENA.

Thou hast a mind that suits
With this, thy fair and outward character.

SHAKESPEARE.

Not yet old enough for a man, nor young enough for a boy; as a
squash is before it is a peascod, or a codling when't is almost an
apple.

SHAKESPEARE.

VIOLET.

Generous, full of gentle qualities,
Incapable of base compliances.

LAMB.

Never did there live on earth
A man of kindlier nature.

WORDSWORTH.

YARROW.

As bonnie lasses I have seen,
And mony full as braw,
But for a modest, graceful mien,
The like I never saw.

BURNS.

Thou art an old love-monger!

SHAKESPEARE.

PART II.

BLUE FLOWERS.

Describing the State or Quality
of your Affections.

ANEMONE HEPATICA.

———

Thou
Art more through love, and greater than thy years.

TENNYSON.

———❋———

Thou art vainly seeking in the open sands of the sea, the pearl
which still remains enclosed in the silent shell.

GOETHE.

BACHELOR'S BUTTON.

———

A virgin purest-lipped, yet in the lore
Of love, deep-learned to the red heart's core.

KEATS.

———❋———

But that you love,
You would not your unhoused free condition
Put into circumscription and confine
For the sea's worth.

SHAKESPEARE.

BLUE-BELL.

My life upon't, young though thou art, thine eye hath stayed upon some favor that it loves.

SHAKESPEARE.

Thou wilt be a lover presently.

SHAKESPEARE.

CHINA ASTER.

A heart as sound as a bell.

SHAKESPEARE.

There is no true drop of blood in thee to be truly touched with love.

SHAKESPEARE.

COLUMBINE.

But a dream,
Too flattering sweet to be substantial.

SHAKESPEARE.

The sweet youth's in love.

SHAKESPEARE.

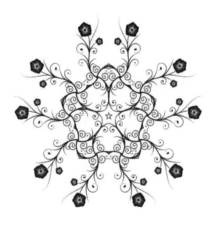

FORGET-ME-NOT.

Oh how the spring of love resembleth
The uncertain glories of an April day,
Which now shows all the beauty of the sun,
And by and by a cloud takes all away.

SHAKESPEARE.

Perfect esteem, enlivened by desire
Ineffable, and sympathy of soul;
Thought meeting thought, and will preventing will,
With boundless confidence.

THOMSON.

GENTIAN.

———

If thou wouldst treat him a little friendly, he would marry thee yet if thou wert willing.

GOETHE.

>━━✳━━<

Young men's love, then, lies
Not truly in their hearts, but in their eyes.

SHAKESPEARE.

HELIOTROPE.

———

Your heart is burst—you have lost half your soul.

SHAKESPEARE.

>━━✳━━<

This is the very ecstasy of love,
Whose violent property foredoes itself,
And leads the will to desperate undertakings,
As oft as any passion under heaven
That does afflict our natures.

SHAKESPEARE.

HYACINTH.

*There are many things which may be grasped with eagerness;
others can only become ours through abstinence and moderation.
Such is the love thou covetest.*

GOETHE.

The worst fault you have, is to be in love.

SHAKESPEARE.

IRIS.

*Is it possible
That love should, of a sudden, take such hold?*

SHAKESPEARE.

*——She alone,
Heard, felt, and seen, possesses every thought,
Fills every sense.*

THOMSON.

LAVENDER.

————

Rich in kindest, truest love.

BURNS.

————✳————

Oh how hard it is to find
The one just suited to your mind!

CAMPBELL.

LARKSPUR.

————

Oh! and you, forsooth, in love,
You that have been Love's whip!

SHAKESPEARE.

————✳————

Never wedding, ever wooing,
Still a lovelorn heart pursuing.

CAMPBELL.

LOBELIA.

Come, come! Wrestle with thy affections.

SHAKESPEARE.

❧✳❧

Rouse yourself, and the weak wanton Cupid
Shall from your neck unloose his amorous folds,
And, like a dew-drop from a lion's mane,
Be shook to air.

SHAKESPEARE.

LUPINE.

As in the bosom of the stream,
The moonbeam dwells at dewy e'en,
So trembling, pure, is tender love,
Within thy breast.——

BURNS.

❧✳❧

The heart of woman is but illy known to you.

MOLIERE.

MONK'S HOOD.

Oh beware of jealousy;
It is the green-eyed monster which doth make
The meat it feeds on.

  * * * * *

——Oh what damned moments tells she o'er
Who dotes, yet doubts, suspects, yet strongly loves.

SHAKESPEARE.

❧ ✳ ☙

If you love the maid,
Bend thoughts and wits to achieve her.

SHAKESPEARE.

MORNING GLORY.

It is too rash, too unadvised, too sudden;
Too like the lightning, which doth cease to be,
Ere one can say, It lightens.

SHAKESPEARE.

A violet in the youth of primy nature,
Forward, not permanent, sweet, not lasting,
The perfume and suppliance of a minute.
No more.

SHAKESPEARE.

PERIWINKLE.

A woman of a steadfast mind,
Tender and deep in thy excess of love.

WORDSWORTH.

Had ye never loved sae kindly,
Had ye never loved sae blindly,
Never met—or never parted,
Ye had ne'er been broken-hearted.

BURNS.

SAGE.

———

More joy it gives thy youthful breast,
To make ten frigid coxcombs vain,
Than one true, manly lover blest.

MOORE.

✐❋✎

Of loving fond, of roving fonder.

MOORE.

VERNAL GRASS.

———

Thou hast nothing in thy head but thy love. Thou shouldst not
forget all others for one.

GOETHE.

✐❋✎

Is it possible that on so little acquaintance you should like her?
that, but seeing, you should love her? and loving, woo? and
wooing, she should grant?

SHAKESPEARE.

VIOLET.

Love no man in good earnest, nor no further in sport neither,
than with safety of a pure blush thou mayst in honor come off
again.

SHAKESPEARE.

You are now sailed into the north of my lady's opinion; where
you will hang like an icicle on a Dutchman's heard, unless you
do redeem it by some laudable attempt.

SHAKESPEARE.

PART III.

PURPLE FLOWERS.

Describing your Worldly Fortune.

ASTER.

———

Tho' poor in gear, ye're rich in love.

BURNS.

><>*<><

You will be—schoolmaster.

SHAKESPEARE.

BACHELOR'S BUTTON.

———

A savory dish, a homely treat,
Where all is plain, where all is neat.

DRYDEN.

><>*<><

Poor as a miser.

BYRON.

COLUMBINE.

Three months with one and six months with another.

WORDSWORTH.

><><*><><

To catch dame Fortune's golden smile,
Assiduous wait upon her.

BURNS.

DAHLIA.

Wondrous rich.

WORDSWORTH.

><><*><><

Argosies—laden with spice and silks.

MARLOWE.

EVERLASTING PEA.

No revenue hast thou but thy good spirits
To feed and clothe thee.

SHAKESPEARE.

———To cast and balance at a desk,
Perched like a crow upon a three-legged stool.

TENNYSON.

FOXGLOVE.

Thy boat sails freely both with wind and stream.

SHAKESPEARE.

Poor and content, is rich, and rich enough.

SHAKESPEARE.

GERANIUM.

Mid the agitated billows of life thou maintainest a steadfast heart.

GOETHE.

❧＊❧

The world is not thy friend, not the world's law;
The world affords no law to make thee rich.

SHAKESPEARE.

LADY'S SLIPPER.

Infinite riches in a little room.

MARLOWE.

❧＊❧

Double, double,
Toil and trouble.

SHAKESPEARE.

LILAC.

An industrious life and ample means.

WORDSWORTH.

A hundred milch-kine to the pail,
Six score fat oxen standing in the stalls,
And all things answerable to this portion.

SHAKESPEARE.

MILKWEED.

———

Bed of straw, and blanket walls.

Byron.

⋙✳⋘

A miser, hoarding heaps of gold,
But pale with ague fears.

Hood.

MONKEY FLOWER.

———

Tend the sick, or educate the young.

Dryden.

⋙✳⋘

Friends, books, a garden, and perchance
Delightful industry enjoyed at home.

Cowper.

NIGHTSHADE.

———

Love in a hut, with water and a crust.

KEATS.

〜✳〜

Rural life in all its joy
And elegance, such as Arcadian song
Transmits fro ancient, uncorrupted times.

THOMSON.

ORCHIS.

———

Open house and ready fare.

WORDSWORTH.

〜✳〜

About two hundred pounds a year.

BUTLER.

PANSY.

———

House within the city,
Richly furnished with plate and gold.

SHAKESPEARE.

✺

A prosperous man, thriving in trade.

WORDSWORTH.

PETUNIA.

———

Peace, and comfort, and domestic bliss.

SOUTHEY.

✺

You can make no marriage present,
Little can you give your wife;
Love will make your cottage pleasant.

TENNYSON.

POLYANTHOS.

An elegant sufficiency; content,
Retirement, rural quiet, friendship, hooks,
Ease and alternate labor, useful life,
Progressive virtue and approving Heaven.

THOMSON.

><*><

Listening senates hang upon thy tongue.

THOMSON.

POLYGALA.

From place to place, dwelling in no place long.

LAMB.

><*><

To roam along, the world's tired denizen.

BYRON.

RHODORA.

Whatever
Exalts, embellishes, and renders life
Delightful.

THOMSON.

⁂

To turn the furrow, and to guide the tool
Mechanic.

THOMSON.

THISTLE.

Happy labor, love and social glee.

THOMSON.

⁂

A pedlar's pack, that bows the bearer down.

COWPER.

WILLOW HERB.

An empty purse, * * *
* * * No money in it.

SHAKESPEARE.

How can he expect that others should
Build for him, sow for him, and at his call
Love him, who for himself will take no heed at all?

BYRON.

PART IV.

YELLOW FLOWERS.

Describing the Scene of your
Future Life.

BUTTERCUP.

In a narrow sphere—
The little circle of domestic life.

SOUTHEY.

In the dissolute city.

WORDSWORTH.

CINQUEFOIL.

A cot beside the hill;
A beehive hum shall soothe the ear,
A willowy brook that turns a mill,
With many a fall shall linger near.

ROGERS.

Fair is the spot, most beautiful the vale;
————The grassy churchyard hangs
Upon a slope above the village school.

WORDSWORTH.

COREOPSIS.

The Lovely cottage in the guardian nook,
————With its own clear brook,
Its own small pasture, almost its own sky!

WORDSWORTH.

Far remote
From such unpleasing sounds as haunt the ear
In village or in town; the bay of curs
Incessant, clinking hammers, grinding wheels,
And infants clamorous, whether pleased or pained.

COWPER.

CHRYSANTHEMUM.

Beneath the shade
Of solemn oaks that tuft the swelling mounds,
Thrown graceful round by Nature's careless hand.

THOMSON.

Where wealth and commerce lift their golden heads.

THOMSON.

DANDELION.

A mansion remote
From the clatter of street-pawing steeds.

COWPER.

In the open fields——
And on the mountains.

WORDSWORTH.

GOLDEN ROD.

A single small cottage—a nest like a dove's.

WORDSWORTH.

A dale
With woods o'erhung, and shagged with mossy rocks,
Whence on each hand the gushing waters play,
And down the rough cascade white dashing fall,
Or gleam in lengthened vista thro' the trees.

THOMSON.

HIBISCUS.

An old deserted mansion.

HOOD.

Your own hands have built a home,
Even for yourself, on a beloved shore.

SHELLEY.

JASMINE.

A cottage far retired
Among the woody windings of a vale,
By solitude and deep surrounding shades,
But more by bashful modesty, concealed.

THOMSON.

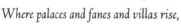

Where palaces and fanes and villas rise,
And gardens smile around an cultured fields,
And fountains gush; and careless herds and flocks
Serenely stray; a world within itself,
Disdaining all assault.

THOMSON.

JOHN'S WORT.

Dear is thy little native vale;
    The ring-dove builds and murmurs there;
    Close by thy cot she tells her tale
To every passing villager.
The squirrel leaps from tree to tree,
And shells his nuts at liberty.

ROGERS.

Mountains, and vales, and waters, all infused
With beauty, and in quietness.

SOUTHEY.

JONQUIL.

A cottage,
Perched upon the green hill-top, but close
Environed with a ring of branching elms,
That overhang the thatch; itself unseen,
Peeps at the vale below.

COWPER.

>✽≺

In some lone cot amid the distant woods,
Sustained alone by providential Heaven.

THOMSON.

LILY.

Knowst thou the house? On pillars rests the roof.

GOETHE.

>✽≺

The same house where thy father dwelt.

COLERIDGE.

LABURNUM.

A pleasant city.

BYRON.

A circular vale, and land-locked, as might seem,
With brook and bridge, and gray stone cottages
Half hid by rocks and fruit-trees.

COLERIDGE.

LOOSE STRIFE.

On either side the river lie
Long fields of barley and of rye,
That clothe the wold and meet the sky;
And through the field the road runs by.

TENNYSON.

Remote, unnamed, dull spot,
The dimmest in the district's map.

BYRON.

MARIGOLD.

A green and silent spot amid the hills,
A small and silent dell! O'er stiller place
No sinking skylark ever poised himself.

COLERIDGE.

—Cottage on a plot of ground,
—With large prospect, north and south.

WORDSWORTH.

MIGNONETTE.

That cottage half embowered
With modest jessamine, and that sweet spot
Of garden ground, when ranged in meet array,
Grow countless sweets—the wall-flower and the pink,
And the thick thyme-bush.

KIRK WHITE.

    In proud, and gay,
And gain-devoted cities.

COWPER.

NASTURTION.

———

In a pleasant glade
With mountains round about environed,
And mighty woods; ———
And in the midst, a little river.

SPENSER.

⤙❋⤚

Where merchants most do congregate.

SHAKESPEARE.

PRIMROSE.

———

In the deep umbrage of a green hill's shade,
Which shows a distant prospect far away
Of busy cities.

BYRON.

⤙❋⤚

Woods, rocks, waves surround it.

SHELLEY.

SAFFRON.

A little lowly hermitage ...
Down in a dale, hard by a forest's side,
Far from resort of people.

SPENSER.

Ships, and waves, and ceaseless motion.

COLERIDGE.

SUNFLOWER.

An old place, full of many a lovely brood,
Tall trees, green arbors, and ground-flowers in flocks.

WORDSWORTH.

Midst the crowd, the hum, the shock of men.

BYRON.

TRUMPET FLOWER.

A fountain, large and fair,
A willow, and a ruined hut.

SPENSER.

✺

In lands beyond the sea.

WORDSWORTH.

VIOLET.

A lonely dwelling, where the shore
Is shadowed with rocks.

SHELLEY.

✺

In forest, copse, and wooded park,
And mid the city's strife.

HOOD.

WALL-FLOWER.

——————

——*A little lawny islet,*
By anemone and violet,
Like mosaic, paven.

SHELLEY.

>✧<

An uninhabited sea-side,
Which the lone fisher, when his nets are dried,
Abandons.

SHELLEY.

WILLOW.

——————

Where quiet sounds from hidden rills.
Float here and there, like things astray;
And high o'erhead the skylark shrills.

COLERIDGE.

>✧<

In the stir and turmoil of the world.

COLERIDGE.

WATER-LILY.

A realm of pleasance, many a mound,
And many a shadow-chequered lawn
Full of the city's stilly sound.

TENNYSON.

  A broad canal
From the main river sluiced, where all
The sloping of the moonlit sward
Is damask work, and deep inlay
Of braided blooms unmown, which creep
Adown to where the waters sleep;
  A goodly place!

TENNYSON

.

PART V.

RED, SCARLET, AND PINK FLOWERS.

Describing the Character of your
Future Companion.

BALSAMINE.

A young heir, bred to wealth and luxury.

SHAKESPEARE.

   A wife
With wealth enough, and young and beauteous,
Brought up as best becomes a gentlewoman;
Her only fault,—and that is faults enough,—
Is, that she is intolerable curst
And shrewd and froward; so beyond all measure,
That I would not wed her for a mine of gold.

SHAKESPEARE.

CANDY TUFT.

His eyes have glorious meanings that declare
More than the light of common day shines there;
A holier triumph, and a sterner aim.

COLERIDGE.

A lady far more beautiful
Than any woman in this waning age.

SHAKESPEARE.

CARDINAL FLOWER.

He speaks three or four languages, word for word, without book, and hath all the good gifts of nature.

SHAKESPEARE.

When she speaks, is it not an alarm to love? She is, indeed, perfection. So delicate with her needle! And admirable musician! Oh she will sing the savages out of a bear.

SHAKESPEARE.

CATCHFLY.

A very foolish, fond old man!

SHAKESPEARE.

A shrewd, ill-favored wife
And yet I promise thee she shall be rich,
And very rich.

SHAKESPEARE.

CHRYSANTHEMUM.

His ruling passion to create the splendid,
He can indulge without restraint; can give
A princely patronage to every art.

SCHILLER.

Will be married to a wealthy widow.

SHAKESPEARE.

CLOVER.

He is true,
He wears no mask—he hates all crooked ways,
He is so good, so noble.

SCHILLER.

She is not froward, but modest as the dove,
She is not hot, but temperate as the morn;
For patience, she will prove a second Grissel,
And Roman Lucrece for chastity.

SHAKESPEARE.

DAHLIA.

He grinds divinity of other days
Down into modern use; transforms old print
To zigzag manuscript, and cheats the eyes
Of gallery critics by a thousand arts.

COWPER.

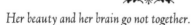

Her beauty and her brain go not together.
She's a good sign, but I have seen small reflection of her wit.

SHAKESPEARE.

EGLANTINE.

He is one,
The truest manner'd; such a holy witch,
That he enchants societies unto him;
Half all men's hearts are his.

SHAKESPEARE.

She's an excellent sweet lady, and out of all suspicion, she is
virtuous.

SHAKESPEARE.

FOUR O'CLOCK.

It is his nature ever to be giving
And making happy.

SCHILLER.

She taketh most delight
In music, instruments, and poetry.

SHAKESPEARE.

GERANIUM.

Heaven never meant him for that passive thing
That can be struck and hammer'd out to suit
Another's taste and fancy. He'll not dance
To every tune of every minister,
It goes against his nature—he can't do it.

SCHILLER.

Two of the sweetest companions in the world.

SHAKESPEARE.

GILLY FLOWER.

A time-pleaser; so crammed, as he thinks, with excellences, that is his ground of faith, that all that look on him love him.

SHAKESPEARE.

She cannot love,
Nor take no shape nor project of affection,
She is so self-endeared.

SHAKESPEARE.

HOLLYHOCK.

He doth nothing but talk of his horse.

SHAKESPEARE.

A pleasant-spirited lady. There's little of the melancholy element in her.

SHAKESPEARE.

HONEYSUCKLE.

He sits 'mongst men like a descended god;
He hath a kind of honor sets him off
More than a mortal seeming.

SHAKESPEARE.

The prettiest low-born lass that ever
Ran on the green sward; nothing she does or seems
But smacks of something greater than herself.

SHAKESPEARE.

KALMIA.

He will hold thee, when his passion shall have spent its novel
force,
Something better than his dog, little dearer than his horse.

SHAKESPEARE.

She is a lady
So tender of rebukes that words are strokes
And strokes death to her.

SHAKESPEARE.

PINK.

By birth a pedlar, by education a card-maker, and now, by
present profession, a tinker.

SHAKESPEARE.

As old as Sibyl, and as curst and shrewd as Socrates' Xantippe.

SHAKESPEARE.

PHLOX.

Is of a churlish disposition.
And little recks to find the way to Heaven
By doing deeds of hospitality.

SHAKESPEARE.

Her care shall be
To comb your noddle with a three legg'd stool,
And paint your face, and use you like a fool.

SHAKESPEARE.

POPPY.

Loose in morals and in manners vain,
In conversation frivolous, in dress
Extreme; at once rapacious and profuse;
Frequent in park with lady at his side,
Ambling, and prattling scandal as he goes,
But rare at home, and never at his books,
Or with his pen, save when he scrawls a card;
Constant at routs, familiar with a round
Of ladyships, a stranger to the poor.

COWPER.

As brown in hue
As hazel nuts, and sweeter than the kernel.

SHAKESPEARE.

PRIMROSE.

A merchant of incomparable wealth.

SHAKESPEARE.

Two; the one as famous for a scolding tongue,
As is the other for beauteous modesty.

SHAKESPEARE.

PEONY.

Three proper young men; of excellent growth and presence.

SHAKESPEARE.

She is a winsome wee thing,
She is a handsome wee thing,
She is a bonnie wee thing,
This sweet wee wife of thine.

BURNS.

ROSE.

———

A strappan youth; he takes the mother's eye.

BURNS.

A woman in her freshest age,
Of wondrous beauty and of bounty rare,
Full of great love.

SPENSER.

SWEET WILLIAM.

———

He's gentle; never schooled, and yet learned; full of noble device;
of all sorts enchantingly beloved.

SHAKESPEARE.

She is like a milk-white lamb that bleats
For man's protection.

KEATS.

SWEET PEA.

A justice
In fair round belly, with good capon lined,
With eyes severe, and beard of formal cut,
Full of wise saws and modern instances.

SHAKESPEARE.

A left-hand, love, imprudent sort of marriage,
With an Italian exile's dark-eyed daughter.

BYRON.

TULIP.

His theme divine,
His office sacred, his credentials clear.
By him the violated law speaks out
Its thunders; and by him, in strains as sweet
As angels use, the Gospel whispers peace.

COWPER.

Graceful and useful all she does,
Blessing and blest where'er she goes.

COWPER.

VERBENA.

A huge feeder,
Snail-slow in profit, and he sleeps by day
More than the wild-cat.

SHAKESPEARE.

An unlessoned girl, unschooled, unpractised;
Happy in this, she is not yet so old
But she may learn; happier than this,
She is not bred so dull but she can learn;
Happiest of all is, that her gentle spirit
Commits itself to yours to be directed,
As from her lord, her governor, her king.

SHAKESPEARE.

VIRGIN'S BOWER.

*He wears his faith but as the fashion of his hat; it ever changes
with the next block.*

SHAKESPEARE.

Oh, but she will love thee truly;
Thou shalt have a pleasant home;
She will order all things duly,
When beneath your roof you come.

TENNYSON.

ZINNIA.

He is but a landscape painter.

TENNYSON.

All of her that's out of doors, most rich!
If she be furnished with a mind so rare,
She is alone the Arabian bird.

SHAKESPEARE.

More Books in the Supernatural History Series

The Wonders of the Invisible World
Cotton Mather

More Wonders of the Invisible World
Robert Calef

*A Report of the Mysterious Noises Heard in the House
of Mr. John D. Fox in Hydesville, Arcadia, Wayne County*
E.E. Lewis

Hydesville: The Story of the Rochester Knockings
Thomas Olman Todd

Spiritualism: The Open Door to the Unseen Universe
James Robertson

Herbert West: Reanimator & Other Tales
H.P. Lovecraft

The Haunted Man
Charles Dickens

*Curse of the Mummy: Nineteenth-Century Tales of
Ancient Egyptian Terror* Anthology

The Vampire; A Tale
John Polidori

The Were-Wolf
Clemence Housman

Found at foxediting.com/books/
and at online and specialty bookstores.

Supernatural History Packs available at
etsy.com/shop/theotherfoxshop.